Contents

Introduction

Almost every country in the world has something beneath its surface worth taking out, and people have been mining various substances for thousands of years. Today, the decline in natural resources has brought the world's attention to the problems associated with mining. Governments and organisations are having to rethink mining methods, and find alternatives to these precious resources.

Mining can be responsible for anything from poisoning water supplies to producing toxic dust clouds or just making the countryside look ugly and scarred.

An Ancient Practice

As long ago as 100,000 years or more, humans were using primitive axes to pick iron ore from the walls of caves in Swaziland, then using it to make red paint. In Western Europe, the Neanderthals burrowed beneath the ground for flint to be used in weapons and tools.

The ancient Egyptians dug for turquoise. The Romans looked for coal for heat and fuel, and searched for gold, silver and iron ore. The eighteenth-century Industrial Revolution was built on the coal mines and iron ore of Europe and the United States. Today, throughout the world, mining brings a great deal of money to people from Beijing to Bristol and Delhi to Delaware.

What is Mining?

Mining is the removal (or extraction) of minerals from the earth. Any substance that cannot be grown by agriculture or made by chemists must be mined, usually from areas deep within the earth called ore bodies, veins, beds or seams. Many materials are brought to the surface by mining but some of the most important are bauxite (for aluminium), coal, iron, lead, zinc and copper, diamonds, silver, gold and platinum. Clay, sand, gravel, granite and limestone used for building are also mined or quarried. It has taken many millions of years for these minerals to be formed so they are thought of as a finite resource – one that will not be renewed when current stocks have all been taken away.

Mining and the Environment

While industry in the twenty-first century is dominated by technology and the production of electrical machinery and computers, mineral extraction is still extremely important to the global economy. Coal, iron, steel and diamonds are among the top earners.

There is a large environmental cost in all this exploitation, and mining is one of the most

DEVELOPMENT WITHOUT DAMAGE

Mining, Minerals and Metals

John Rutter

Evans

damaging industries on Earth. The big challenge for the global industry is how to continue the process while reducing the impact it has on our planet. While mining is one of the most difficult industries to manage in a sustainable way, a number of projects are now in place around the world that are limiting the environmental impact and ensuring more controlled use of resources.

World Resources

% of world production

>25%	11–25%	1–10%	
⬠	◼	▲	Bauxite
⬠	◼	▲	Copper
⬠	◼	▲	Iron ore
⬠	◼	▲	Lead
⬠	◼	▲	Zinc

This map shows the parts of the world where some of the most important resources are found.

Source: Collins World Atlas

FACTS IN FOCUS

African Resources

While Africa has the countries with the poorest economies in the world, the continent also contains many valuable minerals.

Coal from South Africa, Zimbabwe, Botswana, Mozambique, Malawi and Zambia

Uranium from Niger, Namibia, Botswana, Malawi, Zambia, Tanzania, Uganda, Democratic Republic of Congo and Burundi

Gold from South Africa, Ghana, Zimbabwe and Mali

Platinum from South Africa, Zimbabwe and Sierra Leone

Copper, zinc, nickel, iron, lead and manganese from Zambia, Burundi, Djibouti, Guinea-Bissau, Somalia, Madagascar, Ethiopia, Cape Verde, Gambia and Sudan

Diamonds from South Africa, Angola, Botswana, Namibia, Democratic Republic of Congo, Ghana, Tanzania, Côte d'Ivoire, Lesotho and the Central African Republic

Other gemstones from Kenya, Tanzania, Zambia, Zimbabwe, Democratic Republic of Congo, Mozambique, Namibia, Nigeria and Madagascar

These countries are likely to benefit from mineral exploitation in the next few years.

Black Gold

Coal is very old. Formed from decomposed plants crushed under huge pressure and volcanic heat, most of the world's supply dates from around 300 million years ago. Coal has been used as a fuel for thousands of years, but scientists predict that supplies will run out by the year 2250. What can be done to prevent this? And what steps can be taken to limit the environmental damage caused by coal mining?

The Rising Power of Coal

Coal has been used for millennia, but demand for it across Western Europe and the United States dramatically increased during the Industrial Revolution of the eighteenth century. By the start of the twentieth century it was one of the most important resources in the world, and was nicknamed 'black gold'. The United States alone employed more than 700,000 coal miners by the 1920s. Investment was made in new mining techniques and the mines grew bigger and bigger. As the demand for coal increased and reserves near the surface began to be used up, mines were driven deeper and deeper. Different mining methods were developed (see page 10). Environmental damage increased. Unsightly scars were left on the landscape. Important habitats for plants and wildlife were destroyed. Coal began to be used at an unsustainable rate. In human terms, loss of life in mining disasters also increased.

A worker is carried out of a Russian mine after part of it collapsed. Worker safety is now a priority in setting standards for coal mines.

Safety in the Mines

There are many problems associated with mining safely deep underground. These include:

- How to support the roof of the mine to prevent collapse.
- How to provide adequate ventilation and fresh air for the miners.
- How to get rid of the dangerous explosive gases produced by the coal.

Over the years there have been many mine disasters and today there are concerns over mine safety, particularly in less economically developed countries (LEDCs), where the industry is increasing rapidly. China is the world's biggest

coal producer and therefore faces the biggest challenges. Almost 4,000 miners died in China in 2007. The same year, a fund was launched in the northern Shanxi Province – the largest coal-mining region – to support more sustainable mining practices. One of the key elements of this programme is worker safety. Mines that do not conform to safety standards have been closed down or work has been suspended until standards are met.

Workers leave the mine at the end of their shift in China's Shanxi Province. A recent initiative is addressing safety issues here.

TAKE ACTION

To cut down on the amount of coal used to make fuel:

- Save electricity by turning lights off when you leave a room.
- Turn computers and monitors, TVs and other electrical goods off at the mains – do not leave them on stand-by.
- Do not leave mobile-phone chargers plugged in when not charging.
- Burn wood from a sustainable source, rather than coal, in a real fire.

FACTS IN FOCUS

Top 10 Coal Producers

Country	Coal (million tonnes)
China	2,482
United States	990
India	427
Australia	309
South Africa	244
Russia	233
Indonesia	169
Poland	95
Kazakhstan	92
Colombia	64

Source: World Coal Institute, 2006

Mining Methods

Originally coal was mined from outcrops on the surface using drift mines or, if the coal was a few metres below the surface, bell pits. Drift mines were cut into the areas of coal, called coal seams, and accessed by a tunnel. Bell pits were wells shaped like upturned bells, sunk into the earth until the coal seam was reached. The coal would be pulled to the surface in buckets or carried up ladders. Drift mines and bell pits are still used, but in many parts of the world more efficient ways of extracting coal are also used. These include opencast mining, a type of surface mining that was first used in the mid-twentieth century. In this method, all the overlying material on the surface is removed to expose the coal beneath.

Surface Mining

Surface mining is the most cost-effective way of mining, but it can only be done when the coal seam lies relatively near the surface. Over 90 per cent of the coal can be exploited using very large equipment over many square kilometres of land. The covering of soil and rock is broken up by explosives and the resulting 'overburden' is removed by large machines called draglines, power shovels and trucks. The exposed coal seam is then drilled, broken up and loaded on to trucks or conveyors to be used nearby or shipped to other areas.

Underground Mining

Underground mining is more complicated, and machinery tends to be smaller as it has to be taken deep under the earth – sometimes hundreds of metres. There are two main types of underground mining. In room and pillar mining, the coal is cut from different 'rooms' with pillars left between them to support the room. Longwall mining involves mining a large block of coal in a single panel (a 'long wall'). More coal can be extracted in longwall than room and pillar mining.

Coal is found in layers of rock called seams. In opencast mining, the surface material is removed to access the coal seams beneath.

Both surface and underground mining leave scars on the landscape and destroy valuable wildlife habitats. There is no way to avoid some of this damage, but once mining has finished in an area, the landscape can be restored and replanted. Landscape-management initiatives have been successfully introduced in many countries in the past decade, most notably in parts of the United Kingdom, Australia, Canada and Slovenia.

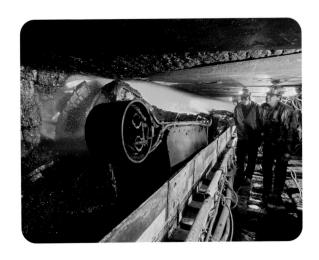

Longwall mining takes place where long coal faces can be extracted by mechanical cutters, called shearers.

CASE STUDY

North America: Surface Strip Mining

In many parts of the USA and Canada, including Wyoming, Montana, Alberta and British Columbia, coal lies in large seams relatively close to the surface. It is easily extracted using strip mining. The overburden is removed and the coal seams exposed before huge bucket-wheel excavators strip the coal from the land. When the coal has been removed, the overburden is replaced and the land may be replanted with vegetation. This is one of the key methods now being adopted in more economically developed countries (MEDCs) to ensure the environmental impact of mining is limited.

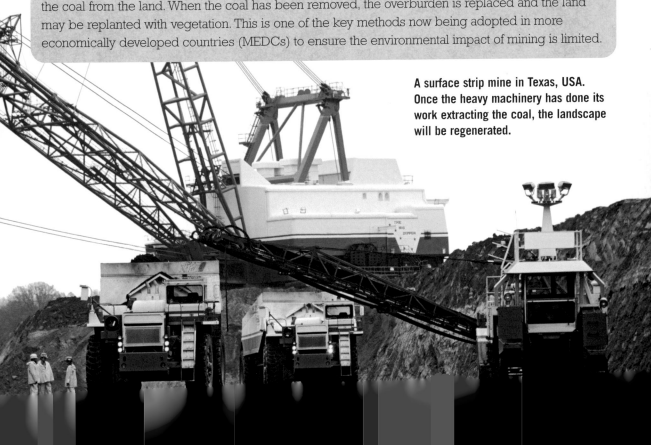

A surface strip mine in Texas, USA. Once the heavy machinery has done its work extracting the coal, the landscape will be regenerated.

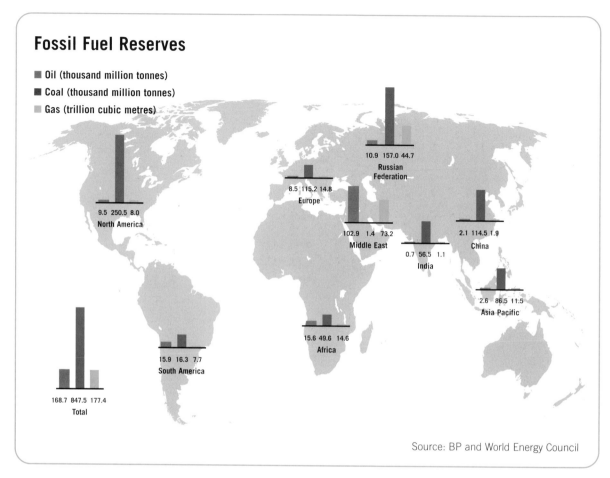

Fossil Fuel Reserves

- ■ Oil (thousand million tonnes)
- ■ Coal (thousand million tonnes)
- ■ Gas (trillion cubic metres)

10.9 157.0 44.7
Russian Federation

8.5 115.2 14.8
Europe

9.5 250.5 8.0
North America

102.9 1.4 73.2
Middle East

2.1 114.5 1.9
China

0.7 56.5 1.1
India

2.6 86.5 11.5
Asia Pacific

15.6 49.6 14.6
Africa

15.9 16.3 7.7
South America

168.7 847.5 177.4
Total

Source: BP and World Energy Council

Limiting Pollution

Since the second half of the twentieth century, coal mining in many MEDCs has been in decline and there has been a rise in production in LEDCs. The top five coal-producing countries are still spread over four continents, however. Worldwide, underground mining accounts for about 60 per cent of the total but, in some important producing countries, surface mining dominates. The damage caused by these methods is not limited to the landscape, though. Burning coal releases large amounts of greenhouse gases into the atmosphere, contributing to climate change. Water can be polluted as waste from mines and the power stations they supply seeps into local rivers and other water sources.

Campaigns by environmental organisations such as the Worldwide Fund for Nature (WWF) and

This map shows the amount of coal, oil and gas reserves in various parts of the world. Although declining, coal will still last longer than oil and natural gas of the important fossil fuels.

Greenpeace have drawn attention to some of the worst cases, and clean-up programmes have been initiated. International organisations such as the International Council on Mining and Metals (ICMM) help develop initiatives to introduce mining practices that are sustainable in all areas – from landscape restructuring to mine safety.

Alternative Resources

Almost every country in the world has coal reserves and it currently generates 40 per cent of the world's electricity. Even at current rates of use, estimated reserves will last almost three times as long as oil and gas. Despite this, coal reserves will one day run out and alternative sources of fuel will need to be found. The renewable energy resources on which most countries focus include solar, wind and water power.

As some governments and organisations seek alternatives to oil-based energy sources, though, others are actually returning to coal as a resource. Coal mining in France stopped in 2004, but two years later an energy company announced it was planning to reopen the country's largest opencast mine. The coal-powered power stations it will supply, however, have much lower emissions of polluting gases.

The Future of Coal

Coal, with its long history, looks set to play a part as the fuel of the future, with predicted demand remaining constant for at least the next 40 years. The biggest market is Asia, with 56 per cent of the world's total – much of this coming from and being used in China. Japan, Taiwan and Korea also import large amounts. As well as generating electricity, coal is important in cement manufacture and for making steel. As Asia grows richer and the demand for steel for construction, cars and household goods increases, so will the demand for coal.

As long as the industry in China and other parts of Asia is developed and managed responsibly, its damaging effects can be limited and, in some areas, prevented completely.

Many new laws have been brought in to protect the environment, but some countries still use old and highly polluting technologies in their mining, metal-making and power-production.

CASE STUDY

Poland: Methane Capture

The processes used in coal mining and in the power stations it fuels release large amounts of methane into the atmosphere. Methane is a greenhouse gas, believed to be responsible for global warming. Finding ways of capturing and using the methane before it pollutes the atmosphere has been the focus of a number of programmes all over the world in recent years. In 2008, the Borynia mine in southern Poland began using methane-capture technology to turn the methane into a fuel for heating and electricity. This earns the mine 'emissions credits', which it sells to a Japanese power company. In this way, the environmental impact is reduced, and the mine benefits from additional income through selling the credits.

Iron and Other Ores

The development of the iron and steel industries has been closely associated with coal mining. Because it requires huge amounts of coal to convert the iron ore dug from the ground into a useable metal, it always made sense to locate iron and steel plants near to coalfields. The fact that the ore was found in the same places as the coal seams made this a lot easier. There are many other metallic ores mined around the world, but the most important is iron.

From Iron to Steel

Iron ores are rocks and minerals from which iron can be extracted. They exist in small amounts on the surface of the Earth – mainly in meteorites from space that have crashed into the planet – but there are huge amounts below the surface that can be mined in the same way as coal.

It is not known when ancient people first discovered how to convert iron ores into a useable metal, but archeologists have found tools made from iron dating back to 3000 BC in Egypt, and many later societies have been judged as becoming civilised when they enter an 'Iron Age'. Those countries that had easily mined deposits – including the United States, the United Kingdom, France, Germany, Spain and Russia – were all at the forefront of the Industrial Revolution.

The Spread of Steel Making

While iron is strong, its main use today is in the production of steel. This is iron that has had most of its impurities removed, and is a much stronger and more malleable metal. To make steel, iron must be mixed with limestone and coal, so areas where these three raw materials occur together, such as South Wales, had a big advantage in developing the industry. Today, with improvements in global shipping, it is not always necessary to be close to the raw materials and this has seen the rise of other powers in the steel-making business. While this has improved the economies of many nations, it has also resulted in the spread of environmental damage associated with mining.

Workers at a steel complex in North Korea. Recently the industry has shifted from MEDCs to LEDCs.

FACTS IN FOCUS

Environmental Effects of Making Steel

Like other types of mining and metal-making, the steel industry can have a damaging effect on the environment in the following ways:

On the land: mining the raw materials such as coal, iron ore and limestone from quarries leaves large scars on the landscape.

In the water: pollutants leaked from mines such as coal dust and fine iron ore get into water courses and groundwater supplies. Factories producing coal may accidentally let waste enter nearby rivers or sewage systems. Windblown dust and chemicals settle in lakes and rivers.

In the air: methane gas from coal mines; other gases from power stations fuelling steel-making factories and from the factories themselves; pollutants from machinery used in mine work and from vehicular transport of products from mines to factories to end users.

Like mining for other resources, extracting iron ore can have a devastating effect on the landscape, as this iron-ore mine in Michigan, USA, shows.

CASE STUDY

Guinea: Simandou Iron Ore Project

The African country of Guinea is rich in iron ore, and the global mining company Rio Tinto plans to tap into this valuable resource. In 2007 the World Bank granted a $30 million investment in the company to encourage it to continue exploring sustainable mining solutions in the region. The money will be used to investigate ways of extracting the iron ore that are less environmentally damaging than traditional methods. Research will also be conducted into ways of conserving the biodiversity of the area, as well as assisting local communities.

Heavy Metal

The worldwide demand for steel has increased over the last few years as many LEDCs, including China and India, have begun massive industrial expansion. Meanwhile, in the once-great steel powers such as the United States, raw materials have either begun to run out or have become more difficult to get out of the ground, and steel-making has decreased. Industrial decline has seen a fall in demand for steel in some of these countries, but the most important factor behind the shift in power has been the cheaper wages paid to workers in LEDCs.

Brazil and China are now the world leaders in producing iron ore, although China is much better equipped to turn the ore into steel so that, despite the huge demand within the country, it is also selling it to other parts of the world. Australia is also a major producer of iron ore, but sells most of it abroad to countries including South Korea and Japan.

America was once a leading steel-producing nation. The closure of the steel mines and mills like this has resulted in high levels of unemployment in areas that grew up around the steel industry.

Steel Recycling

As the cost of producing steel from iron ore has risen in MEDCs, there have been positive knock-on effects for the environment, with a bigger drive to recycle steel-made products such as domestic appliances. Steel is the most recycled metal in the

Recycling steel cans is big business and saves thousands of tonnes of scrap metal being put into landfill sites worldwide.

world and, as well as reducing the amount of waste that has to be put into landfill sites, recycling one tonne of steel saves 1.5 tonnes of iron ore and 0.5 tonnes of coal. In the United Kingdom in 2007, four billion steel cans were recycled, while steel in Europe contains an average of 54 per cent recycled steel and is 100 per cent recyclable itself. Not enough recycling is being carried out, however. In Australia, 56 per cent of steel cans are recycled but each person still sends 3.5 kg of steel cans to landfill every year – enough to make 40,000 fridges. Public education is needed to encourage individuals to recycle more.

FACTS IN FOCUS
Large-scale Recycling

It is not just small products that can be recycled. Cars in the United States are made up of an average of 65 per cent iron and steel, and this is all recycled in the end. Other countries have huge business interests in recycling steel products.

FACTS IN FOCUS
Sustainable Planning

The International Council on Mining and Metals was set up in 2001, with the aim of helping countries all over the world develop more sustainable mining practices. It brings together global industry leaders to share responsibilities in such developments. It has laid out a set of 10 principles for sustainable development, and encourages governments, organisations and communities to follow them. Among these 10 principles are commitments to:

- Conduct mining business in an ethical way.
- Improve health and safety issues in the mining sector.
- Encourage responsible use, re-use and disposal of products.
- Contribute to conservation of biodiversity and responsible land use.
- Integrate sustainable development within the corporate decision-making process.

Even large items such as cars can be recycled, and increasing numbers of countries are providing recycling dumps for large products.

TAKE ACTION

To reduce the demand for new metals and decrease metal ore mining:

- Think about the amount of metal you buy – fill a bottle with juice instead of buying a can.
- Re-use metal containers wherever possible.
- Recycle your metal – collect aluminium and steel cans and send them for recycling.
- Campaign for more recycling sites in your local area.

Any Old Iron?

Iron may be one of the world's most important metals but there are many others. Aluminium, copper, lead, nickel, zinc and palladium (used in everything from computers and mobile phones to catalytic converters on cars) are among the most widely mined and are crucial to modern lifestyles. Many more, such as tin and chrome, are locally very important in regions such as southern Africa and Southeast Asia. Others, like silicon – the second most abundant element on the planet – can be found almost anywhere.

Economic Benefits

Many countries rely on the mining and sale of non-precious metals to bring large amounts of money into their economies. Canada, for example, has huge reserves of natural resources and many of the minerals occur together. Copper is found with zinc, nickel, molybdenum and gold, while zinc is often found in the same seams as lead. This makes exploitation easier and reduces environmental impact, as mines can be situated close together. Canada also benefits from the fact that its southern neighbour and major buyer, the

While making a huge contribution to economic development, there have been many concerns in places such as La Oroya in Peru – one of the most polluted places in the world – that unrestricted mining development has destroyed the lives of the people who live there.

CASE STUDY

The Caribbean: Bauxite Mining

After iron and steel, aluminium is the most sought-after metal on the planet and is used in transportation, building and construction, electrical goods and other consumer products. Aluminium oxide is easiest to extract from an ore called bauxite, found in tropical and sub-tropical regions around the world. Some of the biggest deposits are in Jamaica and other Caribbean countries. Bauxite contributes millions of dollars to the economy of Jamaica but many of the processing companies are from the United States. Other Caribbean countries have no processing plants and export all their ore to factories in countries like Canada. They could make much more money by making the aluminium themselves, providing more sustainable economic growth.

Bauxite is a valuable commodity in the Caribbean, but with more careful planning and management, it could contribute a great deal more to the economies of places like Jamaica.

United States, is one of the world's biggest consumers of all types of metals.

Almost all ores are found in seams both at the Earth's surface and buried underneath, so a mix of surface and underground mining is needed. In MEDCs the technology is often available to make deep pits possible, but labour costs may be too high to make a profit. In many LEDCs technology may be too expensive for local companies but, with cheaper wages, surface mining can be carried out. This means that although there may be large reserves of ores lying beneath the surface, they might remain there, unexploited, for many years.

EXPERT VIEW

'Ninety-nine per cent of children living in and around La Oroya have blood lead levels that exceed acceptable limits. Numerous studies have been carried out to assess the levels and sources of lead and other metals still being deposited in La Oroya. Limited testing has revealed lead, arsenic and cadmium soil contamination throughout the town.'

US-BASED ENVIRONMENTAL THINK-TANK THE BLACKSMITH INSTITUTE

Precious Metals and Minerals

While coal, iron and other metals are the minerals that have made countries rich, there are other resources lying beneath Earth's surface, including diamonds, rubies and sapphires, and precious metals such as gold, silver and platinum. These tend not to lie in large beds or seams, so mining them is more complicated. Their high value, however, means people are willing to put in the effort to get them out of the ground – at a high cost to the environment.

This woman is panning for gold in Laos, using the traditional method of sifting through sediment from the Nam Ou river.

Gold

The value of gold has always been a powerful force in encouraging mining, and it was highly prized by all the great ancient civilisations, from the Egyptians to the Romans and Greeks and, later, the Mayans, Aztecs and Inca of Central and South America.

During the Californian Gold Rush of 1848, most individual prospectors – the name given to the men searching for gold – went panning in streams and rivers, as the gold dust carried by the water settled in the bottom of their sieves. Larger companies, however, used powerful hoses to wash away hillsides and collected the metal-rich water in ponds, where the gold would sink to the bottom. This washed away valuable soil and changed the face of the landscape. Although this method is no longer used in most MEDCs, it is still practised in countries such as Brazil.

Gold and Silver Mining

While gold found among loose soil is easy to extract, most of the metal being exploited today comes from hard rock mining, either open-pit or underground. Gold is also an important by-product from mining other metals. Examples include the Bingham Canyon Mine in Utah, which extracts large amounts of gold alongside its primary product of copper, and the building-material pits in Denver, Colorado, where workers find small amounts of gold while washing through sand and gravel.

The top silver-mining countries are Peru, Mexico, China, Australia and Chile. Much of the silver goes to the worldwide jewellery trade but there are also big demands from industry and for use in photography. There are large reserves in many countries, and demand for silver is increasing, so mining looks set to expand.

CASE STUDY

United States: Cyanide Solutions

In the gold-mining process, solutions of cyanide are used to extract gold from the ore. Cyanide is toxic to both humans and animals, and one of the greatest risks of gold-mining is this chemical leaking into soil and groundwater. Learning lessons from cyanide leak disasters in the past, the United States and some other gold-mining countries now take precautions. The layers of ore are contained within special 'leach pads', lined with plastic, to prevent leaks. After use the cyanide is captured and recycled, and any waste is disposed of in a controlled way. Alternatives to cyanide solutions are also being investigated.

FACTS IN FOCUS

Where to Find Gold

Looking at the world's biggest gold producers shows a similar picture to the other metal ores, with countries such as China, Australia, Canada, Russia and the United States leading the way. There are, however, a number of other places dealing in one of the world's most valuable ores. South Africa has the biggest gold reserves (36,000 tonnes) and while Peru only has reserves of 650 tonnes, much of this is held at Yanacocha near Cajamarca – the most productive gold mine in the world.

This maps shows the parts of the world that produce the most gold. South Africa leads the way.

The World's Main Gold-Producing Countries

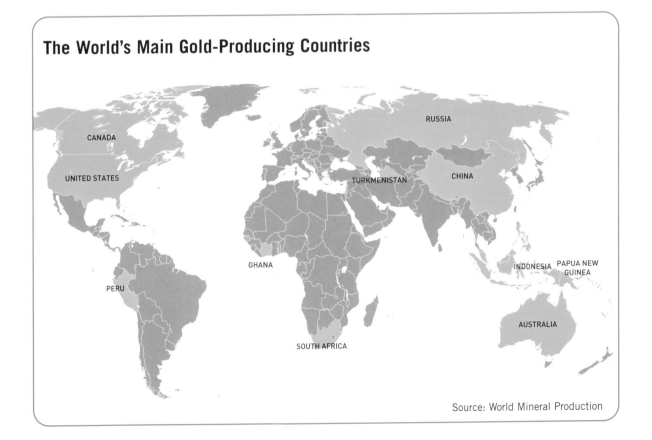

Source: World Mineral Production

The world's largest open-pit copper mine at Chuquicamata in Chile. In 2003, expansion of the mine and increased pollution forced the government to move people away from the nearby town.

Platinum

Platinum is an extremely rare and precious metal – its annual production is about one-tenth that of gold. It is used in the chemical, electronics and jewellery industries, and has become a leading product in climate-change technologies. A major use is for the catalytic converters that get rid of pollutants in diesel engines. There are those who argue that the environmental benefits when platinum is put to such uses outweigh the drawbacks of mining this particular metal.

Copper

The South American country of Chile supplies 35 per cent of the world's total copper. There are concerns over the environmentally damaging methods used to process the ore, however. Smelting the copper ore at refineries releases arsenic and carbon monoxide, which is polluting the air and water around the mines. The people who live in the area, as well as animals and marine life, are affected by this pollution. Accidents in the mines are also common.

It is difficult for poorer countries like Chile to implement more sustainable solutions to their mining industry, but in 2003 the largest copper mining company in the world, Codelco (the National Copper Corporation of Chile) established a policy of sustainable development. This committed to reducing the risks to the environment and workers in the industry. Implementing change will be a slow process but the signs are good. In 2007, two Chilean copper mines received internationally recognised awards for safety.

Uranium

Uranium mining is one of the most controversial practices. The metal can be used in nuclear weapons, but it could also provide an alternative energy source that would reduce our reliance on fossil fuels. More than 50 per cent of the world's uranium comes from Canada, Australia and Kazakhstan and, while most is still mined in open pits or underground, 26 per cent is produced by a method called 'in situ leach'. A hole is bored in the seams of the ore, liquid is poured in to dissolve the metal and the liquid and metal mixture is then extracted.

One of the main environmental problems associated with uranium mining is contaminated liquid getting into local water supplies. In recent years, both national and international organisations have introduced policies to limit such pollution, and now most uranium mines in Australia and Canada have reached international standards of certification. In LEDCs, however, meeting environmental standards is more difficult, and the hazards associated with uranium mining continue.

EXPERT VIEW

'Nuclear power stations have no direct emissions of carbon dioxide and the indirect emissions from the mining and production of the fuel rods and other parts of the lifecycle are also relatively low and in the same order as renewable energy.'

DON ARGUS, CHAIRMAN, BHP BILLITON

Contaminated waste flows from a uranium mining region in Estonia. Liquids from uranium mining can escape into nearby water resources, causing severe pollution.

Diamond Mining

Diamonds are not rare, but they are expensive because of the complicated mining methods required to extract them. Most of the stones are mined from the diamond ores kimberlite and lamproite. The gems themselves are only a very small part of the ore, so it has to be carefully crushed to make sure the largest diamonds are not destroyed. X-rays are then used to identify the parts of the crushed ore that contain diamonds before the stones are separated by hand. This is an expensive business.

Russia is the biggest diamond-producing country, but almost 50 per cent of the world's total comes from central and southern African countries, including Angola, Sierra Leone, Botswana and South Africa. There are fears, however, that some of the stones produced in central Africa come from mines owned by revolutionary military forces and are used to fund wars against legitimate governments – these are known as conflict diamonds (or blood diamonds). There are now many 'ethical' traders in the diamond industry, who refuse to source their diamonds from areas believed to use the money to fund wars.

FACTS IN FOCUS
Global Sale

Because of its complicated supply chain, it is often difficult to work out exactly how much the world's gemstone industry is worth. The largest market is the United States. In 2005 there were record highs for precious stone imports there – valued at almost $760 million. Rubies, sapphires and emeralds all showed huge increases in value. The same minerals were also big business in Europe: France paid out $140 million for diamonds, rubies, sapphires and emeralds; the UK paid $65 million; Italy $48 million; and Germany $28 million. As the richest sectors of society get richer across the world, the market for precious stones shows no sign of decreasing.

Many diamonds end up in jewellery, but they are also used by industry as cutting tools and have many other applications, from dental equipment to supercomputers.

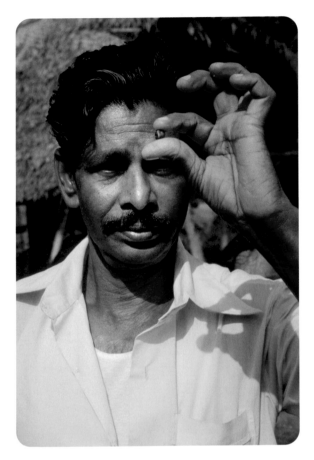

There are hundreds of small gemstone mining operations in Asia. Here, a mine worker examines a sapphire mined from Ratnapura in Sri Lanka.

Other Precious Stones

Other precious stones are found in fewer countries, but they can bring in large amounts of money and help with the development of poorer countries. The rarest of the dazzling green emeralds come from three areas of Colombia; sapphires can be picked straight from the ground in Madagascar; and rubies almost all come from Thailand and Burma (Myanmar). Some countries have deposits of more than one of these gemstones waiting to be exploited. There are hopes, for example, that mining of emeralds, rubies and lapis lazuli could bring much-needed cash to help with the economic development of Afghanistan, currently one of the poorest countries in the world.

CASE STUDY

Canada: Arctic Diamonds

The Diavik diamond mine is located on a small island close to the Arctic Circle. Diamonds were only discovered here in the 1990s and construction began on the mine itself in 2003. As a result, new technologies and responsible practices were able to be implemented from the start. Mine staff work with local indigenous people to address their concerns about environmental effects such as water pollution, and the mine operates a policy of cleaning up as it goes, so land no longer being mined can be reclaimed and re-used by local people and wildlife. It continuously monitors effects on land, water and wildlife.

The Diavik diamond mine in Canada is committed to sustainable mining practices.

Putting it Back Together

Mining is a temporary activity – it lasts only until all the coal or ore has been extracted or becomes too expensive to get out of the ground. The problem then remains of what to do with the land when exploitation has finished. Companies in MEDCs face strict rules forcing them to put the land back to good use, although this is more difficult to regulate and enforce in LEDCs.

The flattened mountaintops resulting from blasting in the United States have changed the face of the landscape forever.

The most obvious damage caused by mining is what happens to the land. The planet is littered with abandoned works. In Russia, where many years of mining took place under the communist government of the Soviet Union, the idea was that nature had to be conquered. The result was that little notice was taken of the damage done to the environment. Today there are concerns that the mining taking place in countries with expanding economies, such as China and India, is causing similar problems. Other countries such as South Africa, Pakistan and Chile simply need the money mining brings – environmental concerns must take second place.

Surface Mining

The scarring of the Earth caused by surface mining has long concerned environmentalists, especially when it occurs over large areas. Valuable farmland can be lost or important habitats for plants and animals destroyed – especially in areas with vulnerable ecosystems such as the Amazon rainforest. Loose rock left in quarries and open mines can also be dangerous to people for many years after work has finished.

Underground Mining

There are different problems with underground mining. Ugly mine buildings at the entrance points to the shafts and the huge amount of machinery used, often left to rot when mining is finished, are obvious indicators of damage, but subsidence also occurs when the surface of the Earth sinks because of the holes created by the shafts beneath. Waste material has to be dumped nearby in spoil heaps or slag heaps and these can take up a lot of space. They can also be dangerous when wet.

So what can be done to develop practices without damage and to reverse the damage that has already been done? One of the key steps is restoring the land after work has been completed.

The land around a former gold mine is replanted with trees as part of a land-restoration programme in Ghana.

CASE STUDY

United States: Mountaintop Blasting

One of the most controversial methods of coal mining is the mountaintop removal taking place in the United States. It involves blasting away the whole top of a mountain to expose the coal seam underneath. Environmentalists have complained that the craggy, jagged and forested mountains throughout Kentucky, West Virginia and Virginia have been changed into flat or rolling hills by the process, while the overburden is dumped in valleys and affects local rivers. Despite the damage caused, mountaintop blasting is seen as a cheaper and safer alternative to sending men down into dangerous pit mines. This became especially important in the United States after 12 miners working underground died in a pit accident in January 2006. Which point of view is right? Should human safety be more important than environmental concerns?

Land Rehabilitation

Making sure old mining land can be used for another activity, such as farming, forestry or building, is called land rehabilitation. When the mining takes place underground it is possible for the surface land to be used for farming cattle or growing crops while the mining continues below. Opencast mining usually leaves huge scars on the land and most of the surface damage has to be dealt with at the end of a mine's life. In Australia, however, there are laws for coal mines, stating that the rehabilitation has to be ongoing while the mine is still open. As the land is stripped, the soil is collected so it can be put back later. Bulldozers and other machines reshape each section of the mine as it is finished with, adding the stored soil then making sure it is safe and will not be eroded. Fertiliser is added and vegetation planted. The cost of the rehabilitation is included in the operating costs of the mines.

Plans for the Future

Not all MEDCs – or all forms of mining – have such strict rules. In the UK's Yorkshire Dales National Park there are a number of disused quarries that have just been abandoned to nature.

Trees are planted as part of a revegetation scheme around a former mine in Queensland, Australia. During excavation, the soil is stored so it can be replaced when work has finished, and the land rehabilitated.

Natural rehabilitation takes a lot of time and many people are annoyed that it has been allowed in areas that are meant to be protected. Nowadays, new rules mean companies must have a plan for the land when they start mining, and many provide habitats for wildlife to occupy when they have finished.

There are different problems with former metal-ore mines. These can leak toxic chemicals and may have to be covered in a layer of clay to stop rainwater and oxygen reacting with them to form dangerous liquids and gases. Open-pit mines often fill with water and have to be surrounded with a fence to stop people using the dangerously deep pits. In some areas there are also problems with subsidence, and ways must be found to deal with this if the rehabilitated land is going to be used by people.

CASE STUDY

Scotland: The Bings of West Lothian

West Lothian was once the centre of Scotland's oil-shale industry. Deep mining extracted crude oil from the rocks and, for a short period, Scotland was the major oil-producing nation of the world. Large spoil heaps (known as bings), 30–90 m high, built up as waste material was taken from the mines. Since the mines were abandoned from the 1940s, a huge variety of plants and animals have made the bings their own and almost half the species in the whole of West Lothian are found on the spoil heaps. This has all happened naturally.

As well as providing a home for plants and animals, the bings offer people space for recreation and leisure.

Challenges for LEDCs

Although there have undoubtedly been improvements in land rehabilitation in MEDCs, the situation is still not perfect, and mine companies often disagree about their responsibilities after the mines have shut. There have been particular concerns in areas where mountaintop removal is practised, such as the Appalachian mountains of the United States. The problems of the MEDCs count for very little, however, when compared with the damage in the poorer countries of the world. Few environmental rules have meant little land rehabilitation takes place when mines are closed. Large numbers of people living near the mines – the workers who could not afford to move when the work finished – are affected by toxic waste in their soils and waterways. Lack of money is a problem, as governments need to spend it on new mines rather than cleaning up any previous mess.

Extreme weather conditions in some areas affect land rehabilitation efforts. In Siberia, where this gold mine is, it is very cold, so covering the land with plants takes a very long time.

Pressure Groups

There are signs, however, that things are changing. Pressure from international environmental groups and from local people concerned about the areas in which they live means governments have to take more notice of the environment. Many of the mining companies working in LEDCs are multinationals with their headquarters in countries like the United States, France and Germany. They have public images to maintain and have to look after the environment if they want to stay popular at home. Australian company BHP Billiton has made a big effort, for example, at its La Guajira mines in Colombia, employing 65 people in their site-rehabilitation plans. The company has also introduced MEDC-style rehabilitation operations at its mines in South Africa and elsewhere. Across the world, people are waking up to the need to respect the environment, and governments are responding. This will be a long, difficult process and LEDCs will need help from the richer countries to overcome some of the problems. Mineral mining has been responsible for some of the greatest contributions to our development, but it is a tough balancing act to ensure it does not also contribute to the destruction of our way of life in the future.

EXPERT VIEW

'The public's and government's expectations of standards of environmental management of mineral operations are increasing. Indeed, the continued development by the mining industry of the nation's mineral resources increasingly depends upon the capacity of the industry to rehabilitate mined areas effectively and to manage the disposal of the wide range of mineral processing wastes.'

BOSTANG RADJAGUKGUK, INDONESIAN CENTRE FOR MINED LAND REHABILITATION STUDIES

A mulberry farm grows out of land that was once an opencast gold mine in Africa.

Water and Air Pollution

Damage to the land is only one environmental consequence of mining practices. The spread of chemicals used in mining processes into water sources and the emission of polluting gases into the atmosphere are also areas being addressed by governments and organisations worldwide.

Damage to Watercourses

Damage to land is usually easy to spot, but when mining activities start to affect watercourses – rivers, lakes, seas and oceans, and underground water supplies – it is much more difficult to see and can easily harm people and the environment without anyone being aware until it is too late. Most of the damage results from chemicals, dust, dirt and metals leaking out from mines into nearby rivers.

In MEDCs there are now strict regulations for the mining industries, and they face heavy fines if they let their activities pollute water. In January 2008, American coal-mining giant Massey Energy was fined $20 million by the US Environmental Protection Agency for letting dirt, powdered coal and metals leak from their sites into rivers in Kentucky and West Virginia. Such examples are an effective warning to other organisations to improve their environmental standards.

Water Pollution in LEDCs

It is much more difficult to monitor similar pollution incidents in LEDCs. Even though many of them have the same laws as richer countries, they are less able to enforce them, and governments are more concerned with making money than protecting the environment. In the South American country of Guyana 'excessive

A copper mine in Michigan, USA, is surrounded by polluted water.

A gold-mining dredger in Guyana brings gold-bearing gravel from the riverbed and separates it using mercury – which then pollutes the river.

sediment from mining operations has turned rivers and creeks near mining sites a milky, orange colour, making them unusable for bathing, drinking, and washing clothes', according to a report from the Harvard Law School. Although there is no specific provision made for sustainable solutions to this problem, the country does have a Mining Act that is intended to monitor and address such hazards.

Health Risks

As well as damage to surface water, pollutants and toxic chemicals from mines can seep through the soil and enter underground water systems (known as groundwater). People then take drinking water from these groundwater supplies by digging wells. This contamination can take place for many years after the mine has ceased working. The problem has affected communities across the world, including those near titanium mines in Vietnam, zinc mines in Korea and the Britannia Copper Mine near Vancouver in Canada's British Columbia.

CASE STUDY

Brazil: The Garimpeiros

Deep in the Amazonian jungle, bands of illegal gold miners – known as garimpeiros – are stripping the land with hydraulic mining in a desperate bid to raise themselves and their families out of poverty. The risks are immense. Laws exist in Brazil to control how mining operations are carried out. The garimpeiros face imprisonment if caught. There are also risks of blood poisoning and brain damage from the mercury they use to wash and extract the gold. On top of this, much of the mercury is washed into the rivers in the Amazon jungle and ends up in the human food chain through infected fish – one of the main sources of protein for the indigenous and immigrant people in the region.

Garimpeiros hunting for gold in Brazil.

A steelworks in South Wales belches out polluting fumes along with condensation from the cooling towers.

Damage to the Air

Although damage to both land and water can be very serious over limited areas, the threats from air pollution caused by mining and the processing of mined metals can have much wider effects. They may even be leading to a change in the way we live our lives through global warming and climate change. Some of the dangers, such as the pollutants that leave the chimneys of steel-making factories, are easy to see but others, such as acid rain caused by microscopic chemicals in the air, are much harder to detect.

Causes of Air Pollution

The main cause of direct air pollution from mines is dust from coal and crushed ores being carried on the wind. This can be very irritating for people living nearby. The problem can be more serious when the dust blown is toxic, such as the by-products of lead mining, or when it settles on agricultural land, killing crops and affecting the livelihoods of farmers. When this

happened to villagers around South America's largest strip mine, Cerrejón Zona Norte in Colombia, local people campaigning against the mine clashed with police and were forced to leave their homes.

Burning coal from the mines in power stations is now perhaps the biggest threat associated with mining, as it adds greenhouse gases to the atmosphere and influences climate change. In many MEDCs efforts are being made to cut down on emissions of such gases, but there is less regulation in most LEDCs. In China acid rain, which comes from the sulphur dioxide and nitrogen oxides emitted by power stations, falls on an estimated 30 per cent of the country and is now seriously affecting farmland. Methane, the second most important greenhouse gas, is released in large quantities by coal mines, although amounts have decreased over the past 20 years.

Transport

There are also indirect effects on the air. Factories processing metal ores, including aluminium and steel, produce greenhouse gases in large quantities worldwide. Many of these factories use power from coal-fired stations or burn the coal themselves. Machines used in the mines are responsible for emissions and, indirectly, the road and rail transport of men and machinery to the mines, of coal and metal ores from the mines to the companies that use them, and of finished products such as steel to their markets all contribute to greenhouse-gas emissions from vehicles. Fortunately, new technologies have been introduced to help reduce this pollution.

Carbon Capture and Storage

The next big technological advances should be in Carbon Capture and Storage (CCS). In this process, the carbon dioxide released from power stations and factories is caught before it enters the atmosphere and is stored underground in old coal mines or oil fields instead. CCS technologies can reduce carbon-dioxide emissions by up to 90 per cent, but they are very expensive. The company FutureGen, set up by several large companies and the governments of countries including China, India, Australia, South Korea and Japan, is using many of these new technologies to build the world's first coal-fuelled, near-zero emissions power station in Illinois, USA.

EXPERT VIEW

'Over the last two decades, steelmakers have reduced energy utilisation per ton by some 28 per cent, and today's processes are productive and green – but steelmakers need to and want to do more.'
LAWRENCE W. KAVANAGH, VICE PRESIDENT, AMERICAN IRON AND STEEL INSTITUTE

An artist's impression of the planned 'green' power station in Illinois, USA. When built it will provide clean electricity to 150,000 homes.

Reduce, Re-use, Recycle

Mining and metal production have harmful effects on the environment, but there are many new technologies being developed to try and stop or reduce the damage caused. Almost all of these are developed and used in MEDCs but, in time, they could become widespread in LEDCs. In addition, it is possible to recycle many of the metals that are mined, cutting down on the need for further exploitation. In other cases, the amounts used can be reduced by finding environmentally friendly alternatives.

Synthetic Gemstones

Because gemstones are so expensive to mine, people have been synthesising (or making) alternatives for years. The Verneuil process, originally developed to make rubies in the early years of the nineteenth century, has become so successful that more than 250,000 kg of gemstones are now synthesised using the method every year. Making gemstones is highly scientific and a great deal of care has to be taken. Rubies, for instance, are made from aluminium oxide but, if it is not pure, the gems produced look artificial.

The Mars Pathfinder vehicle – sent to the red planet on a voyage of discovery – utilised kevlar in its construction.

Plastic Alternatives

Metals are already made by processing their ores so synthesising them is not really practical. During the twentieth century, however, the production of increasingly stronger plastics meant that alternatives to metals became widely available. Kevlar was developed in the 1960s; it is five times as strong as steel, does not rust and is very lightweight so can be used in everything from the car industry to space travel and body armour. There are problems with using these very high-quality plastics, though, as they are often very expensive and, environmentally speaking, the methods used to make them can be very polluting.

Power Generation

There are alternatives in power generation that could help to cut down the amount of coal mined for power stations worldwide. Renewable energy from sources such as waves and tides, wind and the sun is now available on a large scale and is becoming increasingly well used in MEDCs. Even nuclear power, which uses mined uranium, is believed to be more environmentally friendly than coal because of the small amount of the metal needed. Renewable energy will become more widespread over the coming years, but it will need a lot of effort by politicians, as well as significant technological advances, if it is to take over as a major power supply.

EXPERT VIEW

'The solution to the energy and climate crises which are upon us has a name: wind energy. Together with the other renewables ... it can deliver the desired solution ... in the time frame required.'

DR YANNIS TSIPOURIDIS, PRESIDENT OF THE HELLENIC WIND ENERGY ASSOCIATION

Wind power is becoming an increasingly widely used alternative to energy from fossil fuels.

FACTS IN FOCUS
How to Make a Diamond

In nature, diamonds are formed by very high temperatures and huge amounts of pressure, so the same factors are needed to make them in laboratories. In Sarasota in Florida, US company Gemesis uses a tiny piece of a natural diamond, covers it in graphite (the same material as in pencil leads), places it in a crystal growth chamber the size of a washing machine, then heats it up to 1,500°C and puts it under 58,000 times normal air pressure. In three and a half days a rough gem-quality diamond has grown. The gems produced are almost impossible to tell apart from those mined naturally, but they sell for about 30 per cent less.

Gemesis aims to create quality synthetic jewels.

Car batteries are one of the main lead items that are now recycled all over the world.

Recycling

Recycling is big business today and can be applied to the metal used for everything from ships to drinks cans. While steel is the number-one recycled metal, there are many others that can be used over and over again, cutting down on the amount of mining worldwide.

Lead Recycling

Lead is one of the easiest metals to recycle. It can be re-melted any number of times and, as long as impurities are removed, the recycled product can be as good as the metal made from the original ore. It has been estimated that around 85 per cent of the lead in the world could potentially be recycled, although current rates are between 50 and 70 per cent. Its high value means scrap lead is highly sought after and, in the past, has led to a large amount being stolen from old lead piping and even from church roofs.

Recycled lead uses only 35 to 40 per cent of the power needed to make it from its ore, but this is still much higher than some other metals. Producing the very high temperatures needed to extract aluminium from bauxite, for example, is very expensive and it is 20 times more efficient to recycle than make it fresh. As well as saving on mining costs, this has obvious positive effects for the environment, with a reduction in the amount of pollutants produced by power stations and aluminium-processing factories.

Recycling Precious Metals

The high value of precious metals including gold, platinum and silver means it is profitable to recycle them despite the high cost. Unlike aluminium and lead – which are recycled from larger items such as cans and roofing – recycled gold is found in tiny amounts in mobile phones, computer circuit boards and TV sets. Small

- Twenty recycled aluminium cans can be made with the energy it takes to manufacture one brand new one.
- Over 75 per cent of canned drinks are sold in aluminium cans.
- Recycling 1 kg of aluminium saves 8 kg of bauxite, 4 kg of chemicals and 14 kwh of electricity.
- A recycled aluminium can saves enough energy to run a television for three hours.
- 75 per cent of all the aluminium that has ever been made is still in circulation.
- Charities, schools and voluntary groups raise money by collecting aluminium cans – if all aluminium cans were recycled in the UK it would raise £300 million a year.
- A recycled drinks can can be made into a new can, filled and be back on the shelf in just six weeks.

A goldsmith prepares computer circuit boards to extract the gold for recycling.

amounts of gold are also recycled from floor sweepings in jewellery factories and dental laboratories. New recycling technology has made this possible but will only be profitable while there is a high price for the metal. Uranium, another high-value mined metal, can also be recycled after being used in nuclear power stations.

EXPERT VIEW

'By reducing the amount of fresh uranium that is mined, we are lowering the overall radiation dose which the world population receives. And we are also producing around 25 per cent less waste than if we dispose of the fuel after using it only once and replacing it with new uranium.'

BRITISH NUCLEAR FUELS LTD

Technology Fights Back

While there have been huge improvements in the technology of mining and metal production over the past few decades, increasing concern for the environment has meant a similar increase in technological developments to make the industries less damaging on both local and global scales.

Laws in MEDCs have been introduced to limit the amount of direct pollution that mining can cause, and many companies now make huge efforts to reduce the amount of dust produced by crushing coal and ores, and by lorries driving on mine roads. A lot of money has also been spent on new 'clean-coal technologies' to remove dangerous greenhouse gases such as nitrogen oxide and sulphur dioxide. Coal is treated before it leaves the mine to remove impurities so it produces less pollution when it is burnt. According to the National Mining Association, these developments meant some greenhouse-gas emissions in the United States decreased by up to 75 per cent between 1970 and 2000, despite a tripling in the use of coal.

Molten Oxide Electrolysis

There have also been big developments in environmentally friendly iron and steel production, as well as with other metals such as titanium. MOE (Molten Oxide Electrolysis), for example, is a steel-producing technology that is completely carbon free and only gives off oxygen instead of carbon dioxide, the most

Alternatives to coal are being explored in many countries, as the resource dwindles and environmental concerns associated with mining are addressed. This gas power station in the United Kingdom uses cutting-edge technology to enhance fuel efficiency and reduce emissions.

damaging of the greenhouse gases. Experiments washing titanium ore with acid, meanwhile, have shown it is possible to produce less toxic waste than current methods of production do.

At the moment the problem with many of these new technologies is cost – developing and installing such technology is an expensive business. As they become more widely available, however, the price is sure to drop and their use will become more widespread. The main challenge will be getting many LEDCs – where much less money is available to protect the environment – to use the new technologies. To do this, the poorer countries will need help from the richer ones, both by giving them money to buy the machinery they need and sending experts to help them use it properly.

This planned 'hybrid energy center' in Virginia, USA, will use special equipment that captures carbon dioxide before it is released into the atmosphere.

CASE STUDY
Australia: CCS Technology

Australia opened the southern hemisphere's first underground carbon-storage facility in the state of Victoria in April 2008. The plant captures carbon dioxide from a power station, squeezes it until it becomes liquid and then pumps it two kilometres underground into a disused gas field. The rock formations holding the liquid have been compared to giant sponges, able to soak up around 100,000 tonnes of greenhouse gases. The Australian government is convinced the facility will help the country look to a greener future. However, it is expensive and some environmental groups have complained that the technology is not yet proven to work. They think the money should have been spent on other technologies such as solar and wind power.

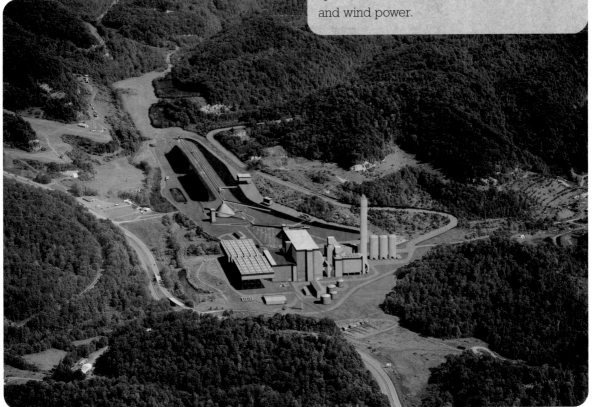

facts and figures

World's Biggest or Richest Mines

Coal (open pit): Cerrejón, Colombia: 690 sq km; 10,000 employees; 30 million tonnes of coal exported in 2007 – 53% to Europe, 20% to the USA.

Iron Ore (open pit): Hull Rust Mine, Minnesota, USA: 4.8 km long, 3.2 km wide, 540 metres deep; two billion tonnes removed since 1895.

Diamonds: Jwaneng, Botswana: 15 million carats of diamonds per year (enough to make eight million pieces of jewellery); 2,100 employees, with its own hospital and airport.

Uranium: Olympic Dam, Australia: around 5,000 tonnes of uranium oxide (and 210,000 tonnes of copper oxide) per year; the largest radioactive dumpsite in the world.

Gold (open pit): Grasberg, Indonesia: originally a 4,100-metre high mountain, now reduced to 3,000 metres; also holds the world's second largest copper reserves.

World Coal Production (2005)

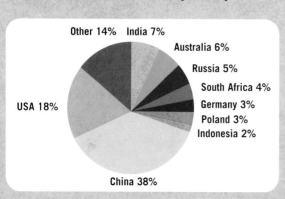

Other 14%   India 7%
Australia 6%
Russia 5%
South Africa 4%
Germany 3%
Poland 3%
Indonesia 2%
USA 18%
China 38%

World Mineral Production (2006)

Top five countries for various minerals and ores

Diamond	Million carats
Russia	38.4
Botswana	34.3
Australia	29.3
Democratic Republic of Congo	29.0
South Africa	15.2

Gold	Kilograms
South Africa	272.1
China	247.2
Australia	247.0
United States	242.0
Peru	203.3

Iron ore	Million tonnes
China	588.2
Brazil	317.8
Australia	275.0
India	174.0
Russia	104.0

Uranium	Tonnes
Canada	9862
Australia	7606
Kazakhstan	5279
Niger	3434
Russia	3262

further Resources

Websites

World Coal Institute
Everything from the history of coal mining to facts and figures on current production.
http://www.worldcoal.org/

Mineralogy 4 Kids
The Mineralogy Society of America's interactive learning site.
http://www.minsocam.org/MSA/K12/K_12.html

British Geological Survey
Loads of information on all sorts of minerals and ores.
http://www.bgs.ac.uk/

Mines and Communities
Some of the effects of mining being felt by communities across the world.
http://www.minesandcommunities.org/

Steel Can Recycling Information Bureau
Recycling facts, news and interactive fun and games.
http://www.scrib.org/

Blacksmith Institute
Pollution caused by mining and metal production in many different countries.
http://www.blacksmithinstitute.org/

Books

Graham, Ian, *Minerals* (Earth's Precious Resources), Heinemann Library, 2004

Hyland, Tony, *Miners and Drillers* (Extreme Jobs), Nelson Thornes, 2005

Jefferis, David, *Green Power: Eco-energy without Pollution*, Crabtree Publishing Company, 2006

Oxlade, Chris, *Energy Technology*, Evans Publishing, 2008

Morgan, Sally, *Coal, Gas and Oil* (Energy Debate), Wayland, 2007

Morgan, Sally, Waste, *Recycling and Reuse*, Evans Publishing, 2005

Scott, Nicky and Axel Scheffler, *Reduce, Reuse, Recycle!: An Easy Household Guide*, Green Books, 2004

Stringer, John, *Energy* (Sustainable Futures), Evans Publishing, 2005

Glossary

atmosphere the mixture of gases that surrounds the Earth, and which is essential for all life.

bauxite the main ore in which aluminium is found and extracted.

bell pit a form of mining in which wells shaped like upturned bells are sunk into the ground.

biodiversity the full range of living organisms in a particular region or environment.

contamination a process in which the purity of something is compromised, making it polluted or poisonous.

crude oil oil in an untreated, natural state.

drift mine an underground mine, accessed via a 'drift' – a tunnel dug into the ground.

economy the system of trade and industry through which a country makes and uses money.

emissions the amount of gases given off by factories, vehicles etc.

erosion the wearing away of natural substances such as rock or soil by wind or water.

exploitation using something to make a profit.

extraction the removal of a resource such as coal, oil or minerals from the ground.

fossil fuel a fuel made from living material over millions of years. Coal, oil and natural gas are examples of fossil fuels.

garimpeiros small-scale, independent and, occasionally, illegal miners.

global warming the rise in global temperatures that is causing climate change. Global warming can occur naturally or be caused by human activity. When it happens naturally, change is slow. If human activity is the cause, the speed of change is much faster and it is almost impossible to manage. The burning of fossil fuels is contributing to global warming.

greenhouse gas a gas that causes the greenhouse effect – the heating up of the Earth's atmosphere. Carbon dioxide and methane are examples of greenhouse gases.

groundwater water that lies beneath the surface of the Earth. Groundwater can be brought to the surface by wells or it can flow in underground rivers and streams until it surfaces.

impurities substances found within a solid that affect its purity.

indigenous naturally found in a country rather than coming from another place. The term can apply to people, animals or plants.

Industrial Revolution a period during the eighteenth and nineteenth centuries when industry was transformed by the use of machinery.

landfill getting rid of large amounts of rubbish by burying it in the ground.

LEDC less economically developed country – one of the poorer countries of the world. LEDCs include all of Africa, Asia (except Japan), Latin America and the Caribbean, and Melanesia, Micronesia and Polynesia.

longwall mining an underground mining method in which large strips of coal ('long walls') are extracted in one go.

MEDC more economically developed country – one of the richer countries of the world. MEDCs include all of Europe, North America, Australia, New Zealand and Japan.

methane a gas that forms the main ingredient of natural gas found in the ground. Methane is a greenhouse gas that contributes to climate change.

mineral a valuable or useful substance found naturally in the ground.

opencast mining a mining technique in which all the excavated material is initially deposited on the surface, but when the excavation is large enough, material from the part being dug is deposited in the holes behind.

ore rocks from which metals can be extracted.

overburden material covering a mineral or ore that must be removed before the resource can be mined.

raw material an unprocessed natural product that is useful to industry. Minerals and ores are raw materials.

refinery a factory where raw materials, such as iron ore, are purified.

rehabilitation the process of returning something to a healthy condition.

reserve the amount of a resource such as coal or iron ore that is held by a particular country.

resource a useful or valuable substance. Resources can be renewable, such as wind or water, or non-renewable, such as coal and oil.

room and pillar mining a form of underground mining in which large 'rooms' are dug and pillars placed in strategic points to hold up the roof.

seam a long thin layer, usually of an ore or a mineral, formed between layers of other rocks.

shaft mine an underground mine entered by a vertical shaft.

smelting a chemical process by which metals are extracted from their ores.

spoil or slag heap a large pile of waste material from a mine or factory.

strategic metal a metal that is used to make weapons and other military products.

strip mining a method of surface mining in which machines are used to scrape away soil or rock to reach mineral deposits that lie just below the surface of the Earth.

subsidence when land sinks to a lower level.

sustainability the use of resources in a way that means the present generation can have what they need without damaging the supply of resources for future generations.

Index